Edward Saunders wrote and illustrated 'The Dental Appointment' when he was just 11 years old. A happy, clever, handsome and fun-loving boy, he dreamed of one day publishing his own book. Tragically, at the age of 18, he died after contracting meningitis and was robbed of the opportunity to become an author. Determined to make Edward's dream come true, his parents and sister Emily have published this book in his memory. We hope you enjoy his humorous tale.

# For Edward

Perfect son, beloved brother
and wonderful friend

First published in Great Britain by Tracey Saunders in 2015.

Project funded by Kickstarter.
Production by Hullo Creative Ltd.

ISBN: 978-0-9932974-1-0

Website www.robeyandthedentist.co.uk

# -ROBEY-
## and the dentist

Edward Saunders

Robey had a dental appointment in the morning but he was worried that his teeth were not white enough.

That night Mum and Dad went out.

Granny and her dog Scruffy came to baby-sit.

As mum was leaving, she said,

Now remember to give your teeth an extra special clean, Robey - you have the dentist in the morning.

As Mum closed the door Robey turned to Granny and asked, "How can I get white teeth by morning, Granny?"

Granny replied,
"You can't get
white teeth
over night.
You need to
clean your teeth
over a long
period of time."

Robey asked, "But Granny, how do you get your teeth so brilliantly white? You must clean them a lot."

Granny slowly answered the question by saying, "I don't clean my teeth because they are false!"

This gave
Robey an
idea and he
ran quickly
upstairs.

Robey went through his dressing up box, scattering the floor with...

Cowboy suit? ...no!

Space Invaders helmet? ...no!

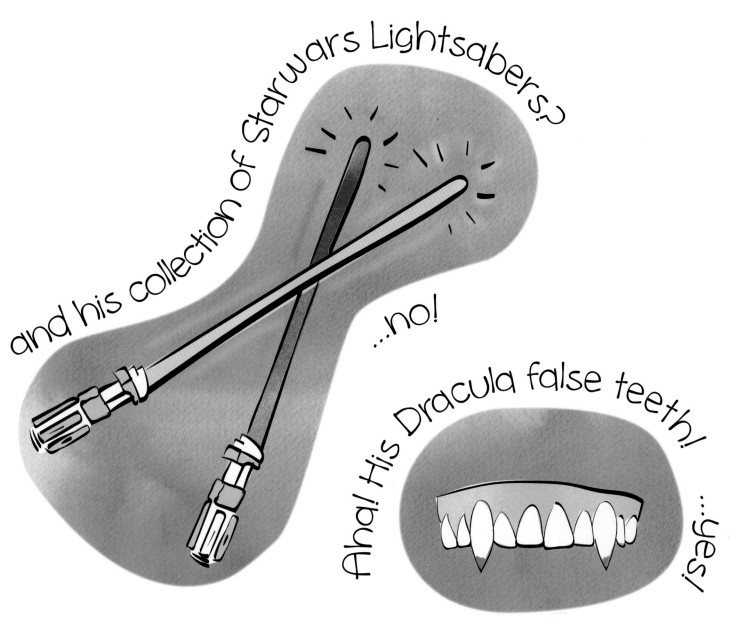

and his collection of Starwars Lightsabers?

...no!

Aha! His Dracula false teeth! ...yes!

He put them in. Now he would have white teeth when he visited the dentist in the morning!

"Time for bed, Robey!" Granny shouted up the stairs. Robey put the false teeth on his desk in his room, got into his pyjamas and slipped into bed.

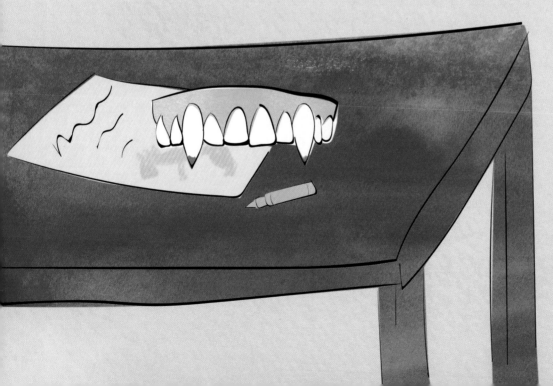

In the night Scruffy, Granny's dog, crept into Robey's room...

... saw Robey's false teeth and thought they were food! He took them in his mouth and went to sleep in the corner.

In the morning,
Robey climbed
out of bed and
looked around.
He saw Scruffy
eyeing him closely.
Robey sat on
his chair next
to his desk.

He looked carefully at his desk.
Something was missing, he
thought. Then he looked at Scruffy.
Something is different, he thought.

Suddenly
Robey realised
his false teeth
weren't on
his desk but
in Scruffy's
mouth!

His plan was ruined!

There was only one thing for it...

Robey got
dressed at
lightning
speed and
rushed
into the
bathroom.

He started cleaning his teeth quickly.

UP, DOWN, LEFT, RIGHT, BACK. FORWARD, No use! UP, DOWN, LEFT, RIGHT, FORWARD...

SNAP!

Oh no! Robey's toothbrush broke!

Then Mum shouted from downstairs, "Robey time for your dental appointment!" Robey gave a big grunt and slumped downstairs.

He ate his breakfast slowly, trying to delay.

But finally it was time for him and Mum to walk to the dentist. He was angry so he trudged all the way there.

Mum signed Robey in at the dentist and they went upstairs together.

Robey slowly climbed into the dentist's big chair and reluctantly opened his mouth.

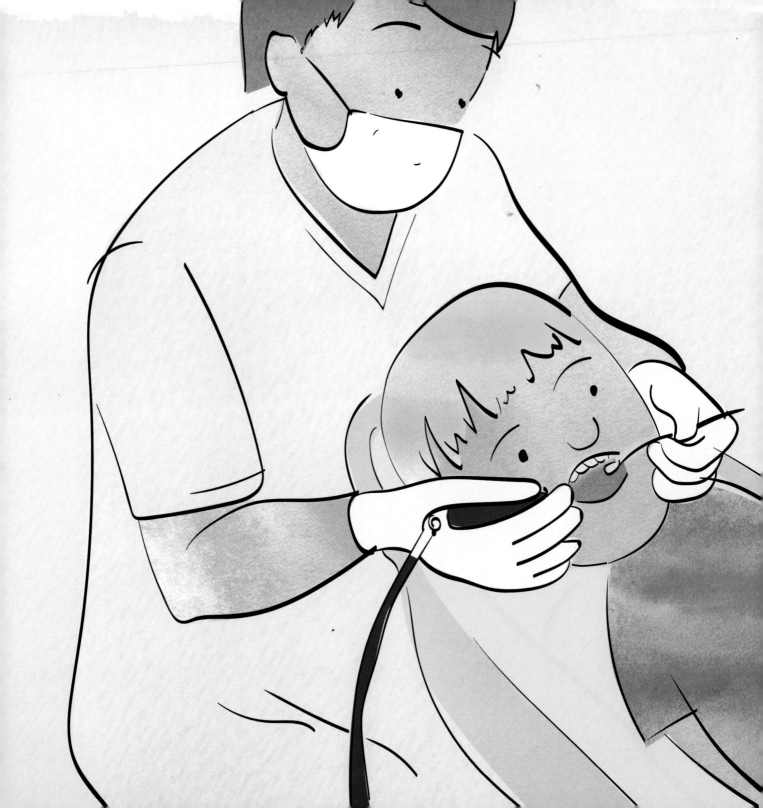

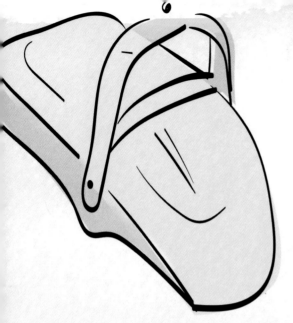

The dentist
made a few loud
grunts and then
said ... "Hmmmm"

Robey replied, "But my teeth don't look white." The dentist answered, "Yes, but not all teeth have to be brilliantly white to be clean. Your teeth are excellently cleaned. Well done!"

So Robey left the
dentist with a

smile!

# Edward's original illustrations

Thank you to the 307 amazing people who pledged their support for the publishing of this book.
Special thanks to those who sponsored a name:

All at Coly House
Declan, Michelle & Maisey Ashley
Ruth Barrett
Katy & Christina Butler
Joseph & Ethan Campbell-Crabb
Jackson Clayton
The Cookies
Lydia Rose Davies
Ben & Ruth Dembo
@Dentalcaroline
Emily Ellis
Lawrence Eskell
Lynn Eskell
Dylan Evans
Uncle Alan Farish
Michael & Amy Farish
Auntie Nicola Farish
Stephen & Carlie Farish
George Ferguson - Mayor of Bristol
Rosemary & David Fife
Danni & Chloe Froude
Kevin Froude
Sharon Froude
Lucy Hamilton
Maisey Hares
Ben Hargreaves
Lee Hargreaves

Nicola Hargreaves
Rory, Sarah, Agatha & Robey Harris
Sally Harris
Heather, John & Ella Harrison
Lewis Harrison
Lynda & Terry Hemmens
Chris & Alex Hemsley
John & Angela Hemsley
Stephen Holliday
Nick & Bev Horne
Tony & Deborah Jenkins
Dr Bill Kellner-Read BDS
Harry Ligman
Oliver Ligman
Sarah Maltin
Duncan McAuley
Rachel McAuley
Barbie & Stuart Moul
Stephen, Katherine & Alice Moul
Laura Nation
Joe O'Byrne
John, Yvonne & Hannah O'Byrne
Max Plummer
Brett Preiss
Anne & Jamie Pritchard
Judith & William Pritchard
Emily Saunders

Granny Maisie Saunders
Mark Saunders
Tracey Saunders
Andrew Sheridan
Hannah Sheridan
Lucy Sheridan
Lorraine Sherman
Sam Skears
Stuart Skears
Chris Smith
Jane & Martin Smith
Steve & Cilla Sparks
Sandra & Kevin Stokes
Adrian Summers & Alison Tucker
Barbara Summers
Charlie Sumpter
Tommy Sumpter
Emily & Jan Taylor
Derrick Thomas the Dentist
Toothfairyblog.org
Florence Wadley
Granny & Grandpa Wadley
Jeremy & Jenifer Wadley
Monty Wainwright
Sophie Wilde

And to those whose donation was made in memory of these loved ones who will be remembered forever:

Pearl & Bonnie Annis
Colin Black
Marion Bond
Helen Cadden
Grace Campbell-Crabb
Amélie Clipson-Smith
Steve Cook
Tom Denny
Aunt Dorothy

Grandson Edward
Brenda Farish
Tim Firkins
Tom Fox
Rita Froude
Maurice John Gilmour BDS MFGDP
Vera Johnson
Richard John Murphy
Barbara Parkin

David Pemble
Edward Saunders
Grandpa James Saunders
Eric Henry Smith
Maddison Conner Smith
Jolene Swift
David "Daphne" Watts
Alan Welch

Thank you to Hullo Creative and Calling The Shots for your support.
A special thank you to my dear friends Nicola Hargreaves and Anne Pritchard for your support throughout.